Dad was painting the back door.
The children were outside.

Floppy wanted to come in.

He jumped up. He put his paws
on the paint.

Dad painted the door again.

Biff kicked a ball. The ball hit the
door.

Dad painted the door again.

Kipper pushed the door. He got
paint on his hands.

Dad was fed up.

He painted the door again.
"What a job!" said Dad.

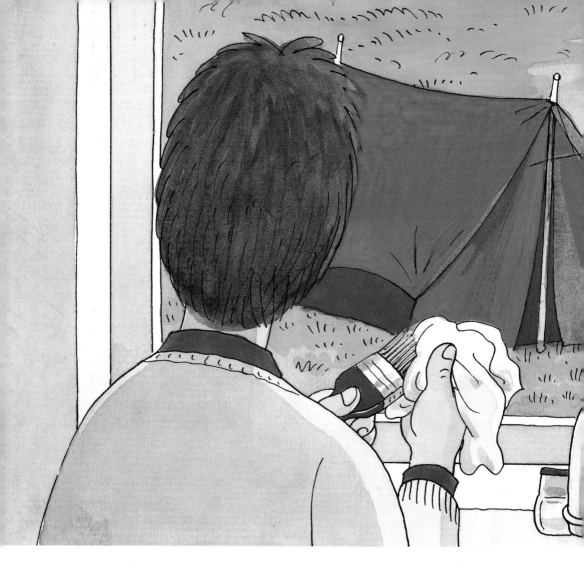

Biff and Chip had a pillow fight.

The pillow split open.
"Oh no!" said Biff.

The wind blew. It blew the feathers.

"Oh no!" said Chip. "Wet paint!"

There was no wet paint. The door
had gone.

Dad had put up an old door.

The back door was inside.
"It's safe here," said Dad.